Purple Ronnie's
Totally Brilliant
Doodle Book

MICHAEL O'MARA BOOKS

First published in Great Britain in 2009 by
Michael O'Mara Books Limited
9 Lion Yard
Tremadoc Road
London SW4 7NQ

A Coolabi Company. www.purpleronnie.com

A CIP catalogue record for this book is available from the British Library.

Papers used by Michael O'Mara Books Limited are natural, recyclable
products made from wood grown in sustainable forests. The manufacturing
processes conform to the environmental regulations of the country of origin.

ISBN: 978-1-84317-393-9

1 2 3 4 5 6 7 8 9 10

www.mombooks.com

Designed by Design 23

Printed and bound in Finland by WS Bookwell, Juva

Hey Doodler!

In my *Totally Brilliant Doodle Book* you'll find loads of amazing doodles of me and my gang for you to finish off and make totally your own. It's great for when you're bored or you just need to chill out. It's brilliant fun to do with your mates too!

All you need is a pen or pencil and a bit of imagination for oodles and oodles of Ronnie doodles. On these pages you'll find loads of hints on what you *could* doodle ... but you can doodle whatever you want!

Hey, why not write a poem or two as well while you're at it!

Love
Purple Ronnie xox

Who's in the bed?

What's for breakfast in bed?

Draw the morning-after face.

Me and Nev practising kung fu...

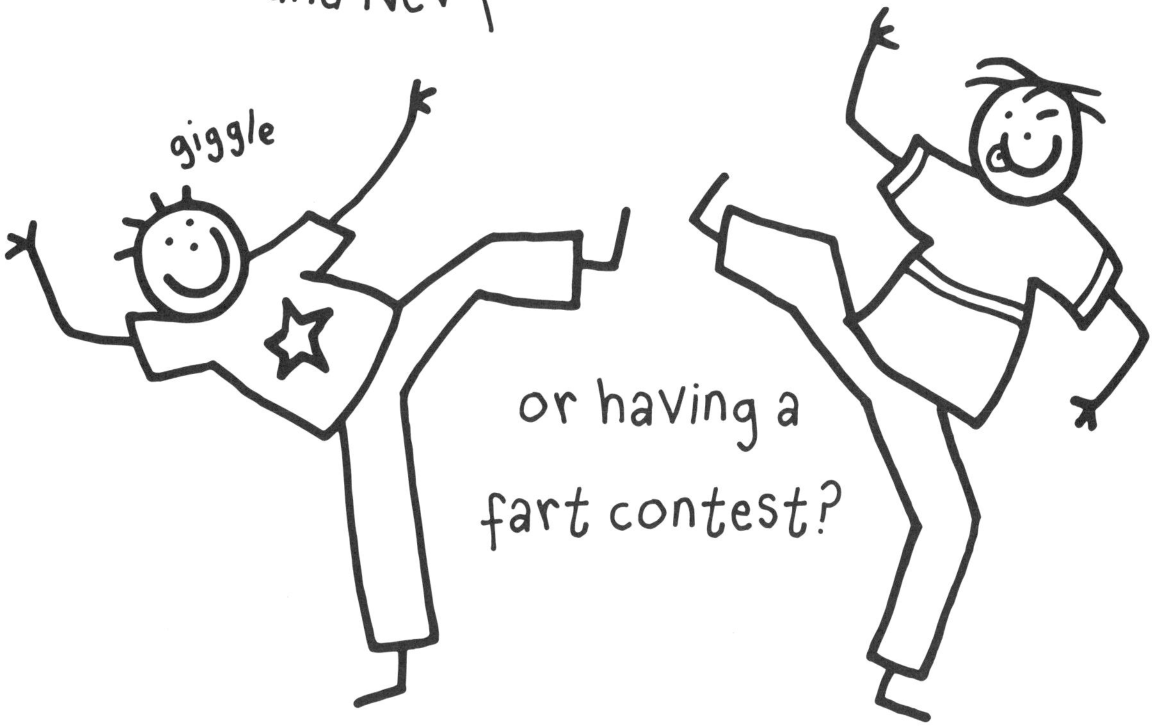

or having a fart contest?

Who's offside?

What's that coming out of the sea?

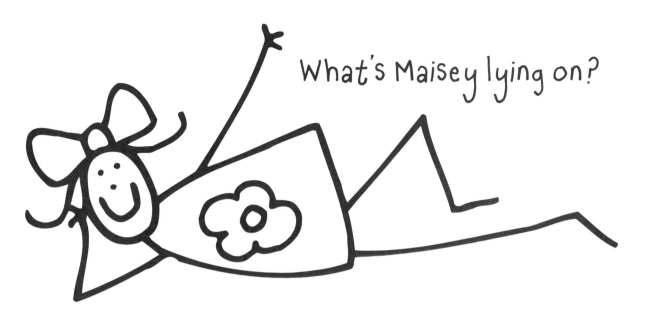

What's Maisey lying on?

Complete the chill-out zone.

What's Ronnie's Grandad so happy about?

Your tummy's spreading out a bit
Your hair is getting thinner

Draw more
mates
break dancing.

wobble

Design Shirlee's disco dress.

Disco Diva!

Thank you for the evening
Thank you for the dance

How many glasses have been drunk?

What's
knocked
him for
six?

Draw out of this world.

float

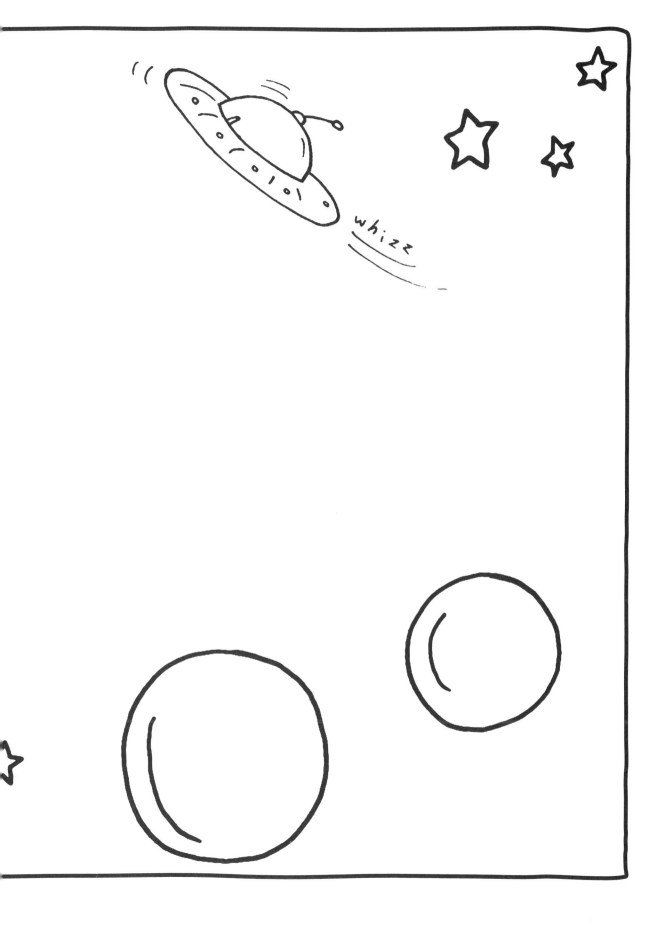

Draw me and my friends out on the pull!

What's on the screensaver?

Design a T-shirt.

Draw your favourite fantasy.

Draw saucy
or sweet.

flash

sparkle

Who is in my motley crew?

← angel

I can be a devil too.

Draw me!

What else do I need for a girl's night in?

Does my bum
look big in this?

When I say that you've got squidgey bits
Don't get cross or grumpy

Who's knickers are these? →

What's on the Barbecue King's barbie?

Who's the lover
writing to?

Add to mum's shopping bags.

You're supercool and gorgeous
You're as lovely as can be
And guess what Mum – the best thing is

←mirror

← star mum

Make mum queen for the day!

Draw your ideal love nest.

Draw more
Maisey outfits.

← hot and
horny
lover

← sexy

How did that happen?

Draw home sweet home!

I'm wearing my
posh pants,
let's party!

Pantastic! Draw more pants.

naughty

cool

love

disco

groovy

... five minutes later ...

You're so unbelievably gorgeous
I thought that I'd just have to say
I'd love to submerge you in chocolate

- -

Fill the party with your best mates!

Draw Maisey's hair styles.

Pimp my board!

Spot the ball!

great
at footie →

worshipping
← a football

nod

leap

What's being lifted?

Who's the running partner?

Beach God ... or beach bum?

Draw sexy beachwear.

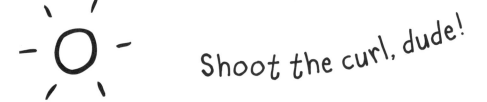

Shoot the curl, dude!

What is our romantic meal?

Draw Ronnie's dream lover.

You're scrumptious and you're sexy
You're fabulous and fun

What are they singing?

Who are the flowers for?

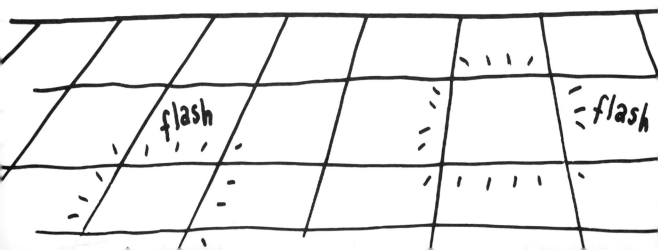

What's caused the brain ache?

Home on the range!

sizzle

Draw a beach babe.

Draw some bling.

christmas
kiss →

Give them some mistletoe.

All over tattoos!

What's he dreaming about?

What's for Christmas dinner?

fab presents
↓

Fill the Christmas sack.

Draw Christmas
decorations.

Build a snowman.

what's below?

What's Shirlee shouting about?

Design Christmas jumpers.

Draw a night out on the town.

Who's the present for?

Throw some shapes!

Where are they off to?